Other books by Jacqueline T. Snyder

Beyond Common Thought: The Joy of Being You
including the spiritual workbooks:

Modern Day Conversations with an Ancient Prophet
Custodians of Tomorrow: Creating Preferred Realilty
The Destiny of Divine Choice
Sacred Knowledge in Daily Living

Soul Enchantments

Mystical Stories to Charm Remembrance

By
Jacqueline T. Snyuder
(Eagle Speaks Woman)

SOUL ENCHANTMENTS
A CADCM / Windsor House Book / December 1992

For information address:
CADCM Publishers
Windsor House
1420 NW Gilman Blvd., Suite 2152
Issaquah, WA 98027-7001

Library of Congress Cataloging-in-Publication Data
Snyder, Jacqueline T.
Soul Enchantments: Mystical Stories to Charm Remembrance

ISBN 0-9625812-1-6
1. Spirituality—Quotations, maxims. 2. Inspirational.
3. Human Potential

Cover Design: Jacqueline T. Snyder
Fire Art by Dolly Meymand
Edited by: Scott E. Miners and Martha A. Prince-Miners

PRINTED IN THE UNITED STATES OF AMERICA

This book is dedicated to the remembrance of the "light" which dwells within the inner being of all people, as well as to "spirit"…those whom I share life with…and those beyond life, who I am blessed to receive and share wisdoms from…

Namasté *

Jacqueline T. Snyder

(Eagle Speaks Woman)

(*Namasté: I salute the light within you where the entire universe resides; when you are at that place within you… and I am at that place within me…we are one.)

ACKNOWLEDGEMENTS

I WANT TO ACKNOWLEDGE, the following people for their friendships and presence in my life... as well as for their endeavors in living their lives with "remembrance" and love, and thereby enhancing the lives of those whose spirits they have touched:

Scott Miners, Martha Prince, Sheila Kenny, David Courchene II, Marilyn and Kim Fletcher, Sunny and Stan Swartz, the Rev. Alex Orbito, Bill Howdon, Dick Davies, Samantha Kurry and Stan Ibrao, Yogi Rajneet, Juanita Kerns, Father Pat, Bill Howdon, Mary Lou Lipscomb, and Suzane Piela; also, with love and devotion for their existence in my lfe, and for being the extraordinary spirits that they are, my sons Sean and Brandon, and, as well, my beloved Z.

My love and God's blessings to all my other family and personal friends and fellow spirits in life.

—Jacqueline
(Eagle Speaks Woman)

CONTENTS

Imagination is more important than knowledge.

—*Albert Einstein*

—

PREFACE

THIS BOOK IS BUILT AROUND WAKE UP STORIES, just the opposite of bedtime stories. Bedtime stories are meant to assist one to sleep. These are stories meant to assist in awakening to spirit, making life more fully alive, lived with the love and magic that is found in spirit, knowing the universe is at our command. These are metaphorical stories with hidden truths, mystical stories that speak to the soul.

Children are told bedtime stories; as children, we knew they were imaginary, yet they were meant to keep the magic awake within our minds. These stories are meant to lift the heart, expand the mind, heal the body and awaken the magic in adulthood. They are meant to bring us out of the anesthesia-like sleep of social numbness and waken us to the universe that responsively awaits our thoughts and words, and our creativity, for surely we are endowed with the power to command our lives and make a better world for ourselves and each other.

May these stories lovingly touch your heart and bring enchantments upon your soul....

—JACQUELINE T. SNYDER

(Eagle Speaks Woman)

The Story of the Spark

People are not simply humans. People are also spirit: God-like beings of light who enter life as spirit...sparks of divine life.

ONCE UPON A NON-TIME in the faraway heavens, very high, there was such a place in which all the Beings on High were gathered, for the Creator of all that Is had summoned their presence—for the grandest of grand events was soon to occur: the continuum of creation! There was soon to be a most important adventure underway on a planet called earth...to ultimately house life and the physical form to be known as man and woman. As such there would be great energy released into the cosmos. These energies were birthed from the love of God

---

and thus they shared the same soul with the source of all life, the Isness. As such, there would come a time when these souls would journey to take the form, the flesh of life and God on earth, eventually evolving to form humanity.

Now the reason all the wondrous God Beings were summoned for this great celebration was to answer one of the most important questions of all: "where, pray tell, would the best place be to place the seed of remembrance, the spark of the divine—humanity's connection to the Creator?" Well, one wondrous God Being thought, "Let's put it upon the highest mountain, for there it shall be most safe. It cannot be lost there, and once found it would most surely be treasured, for it would take great effort to get to the mountain top."

While the other Gods were considering this, they heard a loving, but solemn voice and after softly clearing his throat, one of the Gods spoke, "Ahem, this will not do, for what if one could not climb this mountain? "Quite right," they all agreed. It would not be fair. Why should anyone be deprived? What of those who would choose to come forth and have no legs? They all agreed that it would be folly therefore to hide the spark on the mountaintop, and of course it must not be falsely treasured either, just because it was to be found high upon a mountain.... Its value must be known in and of itself, and this is meant to be discovered therein through exploring all its meaning and power. And so it was, the Gods must still think of yet another location in which to place the spark.

"Ah, I think I have it," offered yet another God, "we will place it in the depths of the sea. There it will continually be cleansed with the lifeforce of the waters and protected therein." Of course, being Neptune, he was a bit partial to this idea. But, again, the Gods contemplated and found that this would not do, as it was reasoned: some humans may not swim or they may live so far ashore as to not even experience these waters, and of course the whole procedure for such a discovery must be very even,

So the mythology continues until ultimately a most wonderous place, important and powerful, to put this divine spark is finally determined. Unanimously, all the Divine Beings on High finally agreed—it would be the most wondrous place indeed, because in this particular place, once it was found, by the very nature of one's search to discover it, it would never be lost again. Of course, after looking everywhere else, once it was found in this most special of all places, it would be treasured the most…for one would have looked everywhere else first. Thus it was determined to place the divine spark of God…in the core of the innermost being of all people.

PEOPLE NEVER COMPLETELY TRULY FORGET. All have at least a vague or distant memory, a sense of something… a haunting feeling of something more, something they had forgotten: it is the spark of the light. That is what makes us weep at moments of

inspiration and joy, and it moves one to help another, engages one in acts of generosity, kindness, forgiveness, love, and it is indeed the way by which our hearts are touched. ❏

Mythical Magical Harbor
The Cargo and the Crown

*Once upon a time, in a place across the waters ,
in a magical harbor, began the story of the
cargo and the crown—*

IMAGINE TRAVELING THROUGH LIFE, and just
as in a vehicle, people can carry in their
mind, heart or within their thinking, cargo,
deep within their self. And so the tale is
spun of such a one as this, one who as such
a vessel finds oneself traveling through
life, out upon the horizons of the sea, with
a deep desire to sail further into the golden
waters of their own potential. Yet from time
to time it appears that the vessel is slow to
get there, and at other times, it feels that it
is simply stuck in the water. And so it is that
what often causes the slowness is the weight

and heaviness of cargo…held in the belly of the great vessel.

Some people vaguely suspect that there maybe some accumulated "stuff" stored in them that does not allow for sailing swiftly upon the surface of such waters.

When, following a moment of familar discouragement, lo, they see in the mist across the moonlit sea what appears to be the most magical of harbors. It seems to shimmer and glow as a warm, beckoning light, and it draws them ever nearer…. In this special harbor, standing on the dock side, there is one who appears very magical and wise, with robes that mystically glisten and eyes that twinkle with a look that mesmerizes, who says, "Ahoy there, and welcome. Give me that which burdens and slows your journey, for that which I am shall set it here upon this dock…. This will relieve you from that which weighs you down. Be not concerned for you need it not. If you miss your troubles and worries, I assure you they can in an instant return to you."

So the person contemplates this and responds, "Well, I'm not sure just exactly what that would be. There is so much that is troubling me, I... I...."

"Ah," says the mystical one, patiently smiling there upon the dock "Well, go within and simply look, look, look." Thus the person begins the inner search for hidden or stored worries and lo and behold finds that there is indeed a whole crate! And it is even labeled "not enough acceptance" on one side, and on another, "low esteem." On yet another side of it, the label reads "noncompletions" and on the other side, close to the very, very top it is marked "confusion." Slightly flustered the person peeks inside and is surprised to recognize within the contents, some issues from as long ago as childhood; and yet, with a deep desire to feel more happiness this person reaches deep, deep within himself and lifts to the surface this crate that is so, so heavy; it is most difficult indeed to lift. Struggling, he can just barely place it into the outstretched hands of the mystical wise one

—

who seems ever so very ancient, confidently waiting on the dock. Much to this one's surprise, the ancient one, with simply one of his hands, and as if the crate were as light to him as air itself, effortlessly sets it upon the side of the dock.

"Hmm," wonders the one who had been carrying the crate, "how is it that it does not seem to be heavy to this one—even weightless in fact?"

Giving just a wink of the eye, the mystical one says to this person, "Now go back within and find what else slows your journey and feels heavy in the vessel of your being.... You may want to check closely around your abdomen." And so he does, and sure enough he finds yet another crate there as well. This one is labeled "nurturing needed" on one side, "not enough love" on another side, "unsatisfied" on still another, and on the last side, it says "judgement."

With loving kindness this mystical one explains to him all this stored in the belly is very hard to digest, and that many people try mistakenly to feed these emotions with

more foodstuffs, brew, and so forth, causing many ailments.... Rightful action is far more important. And so the person reaches down into the belly of his vessel, and he carefully lifts up this crate, which, although it is a bit smaller, is still quite heavy. After great effort, he finally hands his crate up again and gives it to the ancient one, who accepts it with such great ease, that with one finger he spins it around in the air with a sparkling swirl of what could be considered fairy dust, and floats it precisely over on the dock next to the other crate.

With his smile beaming even broader (if that was at all possible) and a slight trace of mischief in his twinkling eyes, the ancient one says to him, "You are doing quite well. Do continue" he says, "Go again within and find more of that which is your burdens."

So deeper within, and particularly around the areas of the sexual organs, the person finds another crate. This one is very, very full. On one side it is marked "guilt," on another it says "unfulfilled," and on yet another side it is marked "inappropriate."

On the last side, very, very close to the top the label is marked "frustration."

The ancient one, softly clearing his throat, patiently, and with a fatherly sort of compassion, says, "Do take your time. I will wait, for this is very heavy and very deep within you. You must bring all of its content completely to the surface. I do very much understand the sensitivity of these issues... for they hold for many people a strong identity of the self. But, pray tell, do put forth this effort to do so. I assure you, you will feel much better."

So the person starts to reach very, very deep, and it is a most difficult task indeed to bring up to the surface this crate, for it is well packed, and very closed off, very hidden. Finally, with great strain he lifts it up, up, up and with immense relief, hands it over to the wise one who sort of reaches for it as if he too is to have a bit of an exertion himself, just to confirm to the person handing the cargo over that it is as heavy as they suppose it to be. But then, much to the person's surprise, the ancient one whimsically twirls the crate in the air, flips it around over his shoulder, and magically floats it right over to there the other craates are accumulating upon the dock.

The ancient one says, "Now that you have emptied out such a great amount of your stored cargo, your heavy baggage, you can see that these particular parts of your life do not necessarily fuel you to those golden waters on the horizon of your potential. Also, because you have trusted and given your heavy cargo to me, I have something other to tell you. Take notice: Do you feel now the bouyance and the lightness in your vessel? Ah! You shall see now it can make much greater and smoother sailing speed with far less effort."

Then, almost instantly, this person feels as if he is drifting away from the dockside and this magical harbor. He looks fondly back at all the crates of cargo stacked there that were within his being, and he wonders, "Well, but … should I leave this? What if I need it? I used so much of it as a means to

relate to others. Also, this cargo has been in my family a long time. In fact, I'm sure I inherited some of it."

A very understanding look is given from the ancient one standing upon the dock, who, it seems, also has the power to know this one's inner thoughts as well, knowing all about the crates of stuff he had heretofore stored within himself. The mystical one says "Ah, well, it matters not so much all that which has been inside of your family and handed down to you for generations; familiar as it is to you, and comforting as it may be, in the golden horizons of your potential you will find other new cargos. You will also discover the possession of wisdoms and insights that come from another heritage, the heritage of light that shines within you and the golden light upon the water. But if you fear that you might indeed miss that which is stacked upon this dock, I would have you check within your heart before you depart to see what you have left there misunderstood, and momentarily, if you will, learn their true

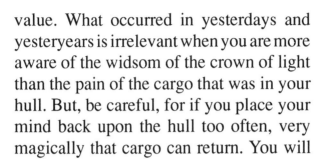

value. What occurred in yesterdays and yesteryears is irrelevant when you are more aware of the widsom of the crown of light than the pain of the cargo that was in your hull. But, be careful, for if you place your mind back upon the hull too often, very magically that cargo can return. You will then think you need to return to this magical, mystical harbor and get rid of this again."

So the person looks into their heart, thinking, "Hm, what could he mean? Well, there is a learning I feel that came from unloading that cargo over there...and here is a wisdom that must have come from...I'm not sure where. Ooh, and here is a little residue of pain; this is causing a little bit of discomfort here. This might have just been from carrying those crates all this time."

Then the magical one says, "Hand it to me, for this pain has an inherited habit, and it can attract experiences to itself and back again, to justify its own existence."

So, the person gives up the pain and releases it from the heart and extends it to the ancient one—but surprisingly he doesn't take it; instead he gently cradles it in his cupped hands as he looks at it, and then gazes up into the face of the one who took it from his heart, and, with his now so familiar smile and wizard-like gaze, says, "My oh my. This looks like it is filled with wondrous gems. It looks to me like the growth of enlightenment and a truly spiritual human being. How very precious the living of your life experiences have been." He then scrutinizes it very closely, and, with a majestic wave of his hand, along with that familiar fairy dust, turns it into many beauteous gems; then, with a blink of his twinkling eye, the gems are within a glorious crown; not an ordinary crown, but a crown of wondrous light—and the gems are not solid, but they are gems of light. There is green, red, and yellow, blue, purple, and pink, and many more colors, and they are all within this dazzling crown of lights.

The ancient one reaches over and sets the crown upon the head of the person who is about to set sail, and he says to this one, "Hmm. This looks rather wonderful to me....It's wisdom that turns pain into gems. Just when you feel completed with it...poof! it will change into something else: something like compassion or understanding or forgiveness, and, of course, my favorite of all, love. All are gems of wisdom. Let this crown guide you in its light. Let this indeed navigate and chart your course. Whenever you are in doubt, project your focus by the path of your heart up into your crown of light — your many faculties of higher awareness— for there is within your heritage of light the ability to heal thyself, to access guidance for that which is your individual beingness and for the good of all humanity. It holds that which is great creativity, so you will be guided to know exactly, indeed, what is for your most joy and divine purpose as you enter back into the golden waters of life. Whenever you project yourself upward, you reattune yourself to the navigator within you...your own light, your spirit."

Deeply touched by such knowledge, the one who is about to set sail sat silently awhile… and then looked slyly up into the face of this wise one and said, "What about this, this stuff that I have carried and am about to leave behind upon the dock? Inside those crates…it is my stuff…I think it is my identity; it has been with me so long—and, and…well…I am not sure, but I think I have grown sort of fond of it."

With a knowing chuckle, the wise one says, "Not really. You have just become familiar with it and you are confused about the two. 'Familiar' and 'fondness' are not exactly the same. But I will have you to know, that which sits upon your head is what you have learned from living and from carrying this cargo and the experience of it. So you take your wisdoms with you, within these various lights, and you don't need to remember all the minute details of your pain; you need only the new found wisdom that has been accumulated from it."

Realizing this truth, with relief, the person begins to feel the buoyancy of his vessel and the joyous anticipation of the journey

that is to be. He is reminded by the ancient one, that all that he has previously sailed— all the various experiences upon all the waters: the storms, hurricanes, shallow waters with rocky bottoms—all that has been in his journey previous to this magical harbor are experiences that have helped create the golden waters to be seen now.

And so, at last, with a misty look within his eye, the owner of the vessel, the being, casts his vision toward the golden waters of his divine potential. He is beginning to drift further away now from the dock, and wonders what is to become of his old friend, this magical one. And he yells back, "Oh, oh ancient one . . . but I will miss you."

The ancient one says, "Ah, look not for me here as you perceive me to be...but rather, how I most truly am...and you shall sense me yonder...for I dwell within the brightness of the golden light upon the horizon.... And I hold a place for you and all people there.

Remember to sail joyously now the sea of

life, giving love and kindness to all you meet on your journey....

— 🌱 —

HOLDING CARGO IN THE BELLY OF THE VESSEL is akin to holding old stuff in the psyche. It makes the body heavy and often unable to function properly.

The wise one on the dock knows the illusions of the crates, even though the one who carries them is so fixed on them that they become their reality.

Be cautious of your cargo. It can sink you; or, at the very least, slow down your journey. Also, be sure to inspect for damaged goods, discarding what is no longer healthy for you, and reevaluate the purposefulness of what you decide to store within the hull of your psyche.

God speed— and bon voyage. ❏

The Costume Ball of Life

*I*N THE AUTUMN, *the season of frosty nights, falling leaves, pumpkins and the trick or treat of Halloween, my youngest son was very excited as to what to create as a costume disguise for the customary trick or treat. As I contemplated this, a story came to mind about how we as human beings, in a sense, are going through life in the various costumes we have created. The following is a story told for all the truths woven within it.*

ONCE UPON A TIME there was going to be a wondrous "ball" called life, and this would be the expansion of God into the remarkable adventure called humanness. As such, the adventure has been underway here for what seems like forever. Many souls have come to the grand ball of life and many by choice

———

have left it. Those who attended this ball all had the ability to make, or imagine costumes in order to accomodate their spirit into physical form.

In the beginning there was less of a selection of "costumes," because spirits at the time were very young and naive in what it meant to be human, and imagination was yet to evolve; nonetheless, the costumes in the ball have become quite creative through the flow of time and are like the costumes of those who on Halloween desire to go into the world to have a treat or a trick. Costumes of all shapes, sizes, and colors, creating a variety of cultures, formed the human race. As the ball of life is underway many spirits begin to arrive; some stay longer than others, just as some need to leave early to learn and rest—and heal by assimilating what they have experienced through the interplay with the others at the ball, until such time as the opportunity arises to return again in yet a different costume, or disguise, for another part, as in a character role in a theatre play, and experience a different perspective of the adventure of life.

Some of those who have been at the ball for sometime begin to look at their costumes and find less and less favor with them. Searching for something to do, they start the game of comparison, which is not all together a fun game, for those who start doubting their original choice of expression began thinking: "Why didn't I pick a different costume than this, or even that costume; it is much more beauteous than mine and still this other one appears to even pay more... I wonder if I picked the right one?" Hmmm.

As self judgement grew, they began to find less and less favor with themselves. This diminished their desire to be at the ball, as the joy and fun seemed to decrease and the unfavorable comparisons grew, sadly, for what started out to be a costume to attend the ball and live, now began to feel limited and confining. Because of their preoccupation with their physical appearance they quite forgot they had

---

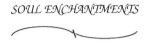

existence before the costume was created.

In other civilizations, hundreds of years earlier, there were those at the ball who desired freedom. They decided that the ball could be enlarged a bit, perhaps if there were more lands; so, they traveled across waterways and found other lands. This created more of an adventure. More came into the human experience.

As the adventure was getting underway, some at the ball decided they needed to be more organized, thinking, "This ball was very uncivilized." So it was put into motion that there should be elected those who would implement certain rules that everyone was to agree upon. Well, at the time that sounded reasonable, and, as long as everyone could agree upon it, it seemed fair. So they set about to do this very thing, and, when most all agreed, it was decreed that certain individuals would be the authorities of the ball. It was hoped that those selected would be strong in their faith and they would govern so there would be equality and justice at this ball—and only a

small, necessary amount of rules and laws. Only, as time went by something went wrong, for what was put into motion as law for civility eventually became less civilized and some of the "authorities" and their governing became corrupted and thus less civilized than those who originated their role. And so it seemed the very people for whom the laws were created to benefit were now the last to be considered or consulted about changes in the rules.

So there began a further sense of dissatisfaction among those who were at the ball. Of course, it is important to remember, through the flow of time, that those attending the ball had forgotten the original purpose for the ball... so disillusionment was surely to follow. For, you see, the longer they spent in life in costume... the less and less they remembered of their spirit and its magic....

Thus, having forgotten this, they became very distressed as their costumes grew old and tattered with age, and out of this, the false belief of thinking they were only their costumes, the fear of death was born; and their joy and living life in the moment, for many... ceased to be. The effect of this fear was to make them so much, much less alive.

Life at the ball went on, and as, one by one, they found their costume becoming aged and tattered; they felt shamed and wanted to avoid being seen, for you see everyone had become so civilized at the ball, that old tattered costumes weren't considered as valuable as they were meant to be.... So... many hid them. Many different illnesses and sicknesses grew from lack of love, fear of aging, death and non-acceptance at this ball. There were, as well, more human rules than could be lived in freedom and still allow one to sustain their uniquenesses and their individuality, and so everyone became more and more alike at the ball..., as "differences" were less and less valued.

So they started finding ways to adjust and alter their costumes so they looked more alike, and when they saw that certain

costumes were more prospered and coveted than others, they tried to decorate their costume to be more like them, and those who did not know how to do that continued to live in such a way as to avoid the stares of others—imagined or real—as the feeling inside hurt...so they wanted to hide. They found very creative ways to live . . . and not be alive. As their self-images shrank, so did their joy and the ability to remember their spirit and why oh why they ever chose to come to the ball....

Eventually the rules and laws at the ball of life became so distorted and, unfortunately, to many of those who governed, even more important than people themselves. Those at the ball who learned all the rules, memorized the rules, and lived by the rules, wanted to make sure that everybody else did too: for if someone has devoted their whole life to understanding a certain set of these rules and living them, they of course want to make sure that the person next door to them does the same thing, so that they have not learned, studied, and memorized

these rules for no reason. This is particularly so if they have erroneously conformed to and lived them for someone else's acknowledgement or approval, placing more value there than in their own inner sense of rightfulness.

Yet what of the most important and basic rule of Law...the one that allows for the freedom and love of spirit. The true law of life, given by the Supreme Authority, the giver of the ball of life...had been forgotten along with the forgetfulness of their own spirit.

Time flows further in this ball, and, eventually, as it flows, messengers—spirits who remember what those before them forgot—are sent to attend the ball and to guide and to teach that which will bring the joy of recall to the spirits who had forgotten.

Eventually, despite all else that is taking place, imagine some people at the ball who begin to have original thoughts. In that original thought, they seem to remember something about being unique, something about God. They find the more they contemplate this, the better they start to feel…, and the more they begin to remember!

With a sense of excitement and wonder, one of those who started to remember clears his throat and says… "I…I think there is more to us than what appears to be just our costumes."

"Shhh!" says one of the "authorities" who happened by and overheard: "No, no, no. You must be crazy, or you are not well. You are acting as a radical, extreme." This is followed by looks of annoyance from others to signal him that he must be very quiet about how he is feeling, or he won't be very accepted and approved of at the ball.

So, he decides to himself, "That's alright. This ball is a little stuffy at times anyway." He looks out the window of the great ballroom and he sees nature…as if for the first time, and he decides to take himself out into the courtyard. Once there he can hear the birds singing, and he notices the water in the creek nearby; Ah, it feels

---

wondrous to be there, and he finds that while he is there among nature, these thoughts of remembrance get better. Ah! He has learned something: the value of solitude in nature—that it's very conducive to personal knowing..., or is it just remembering...?

Eventually someone from inside the ballroom, notices and wonders, "Who is that out there in the courtyard?" And yet another person goes to find out, and says "I wonder what you are doing out here?"

And this one says, "Well, I had an original thought while I was inside, and it seems that it is not encouraged by certain people in the ball...so, I came out here with nature to be with my thoughts."

"Hmm...I think I've had a similar experience before also just like that!"

He says, "Really? Tell me about it."

So, he tells him, "Well, you know, I was wondering about health: why do we have to be sick? Where does God fit into all of this?"

"Precisely the thought I've had as well. I've been thinking the same thing! Only it's best we be cautious.They don't seem to want to hear it back in there, so don't talk too loudly...."

As time flows by more and more people seeking a better way of life gradually find their way out into the courtyard to be with nature more, until eventually there are just about as many people in the courtyard as there are in the ballroom. The ones in the courtyard are thinking, questioning, and sharing their deepening concerns for their well being and the possibilities for new attitudes and approaches for this to be so.

While back in the ballroom most of the authorities are busy wondering how they are going to be reinstated to keep their power to control and rule others, which of course leaves them little time for much else, such as spiritual ideas or solitude with nature.... Until, from being under such stress, one of the authorities becomes sick and overcome with concern, for he doesn't want to die. His fear of death is older and

greater than is his fear of change...so, reflective thinking became his new way. He found his conscience bothered him because he realized he hadn't really truly lived: "there must be so much more to life," he thought, and he begins to remember the simpler joys of his childhood and the promises he made to himself about what he would do when he grew up, and vaguely there was something else...what was it...? If only he could remember....

Returning his focus to his concern for his own poor health, he recalled and contemplated about a few of his colleagues who had tried these new experimental drugs and others who had these supposedly wonderful operations, but sometimes things went wrong: some died; they weren't here anymore. Frustrated, he begins to think and worry that there is no place you can turn to, and there's no one you can trust. Well, after all, if you can't completely trust your government anymore and you can't totally depend on drugs and your medical system, what can you do? Who can you trust...?

Then a thought, like an inner voice of guidance seems to come to him, "Why don't you go see what they are doing in the courtyard? Why not listen in and learn...?"

And so, out of absolute desperateness, and being convinced that it is a matter of absolute desperateness, when he thinks no one is looking his way, he quietly and cautiously steps out into the courtyard where he had heard something odd and different was occuring. He doesn't go too close, rather, he hangs around the perimeters hoping to over hear what they may be saying about health and healing.

Surprisingly, he notices something he never noticed before when he was inside the ballroom looking out into the courtyard, "Well, these people don't look so radical. There are some even wearing suits similar to mine. They can't be all that bad. That one over here in old dungarees looks like a fisherman, and oh my, there's a doctor here too!" There were also teachers, lumbermen, students, waiters, builders, other doctors, dentists, lawyers and professionals just like himself, and much to his dismay, he wondered why he never noticed there were just common, normal people, except they seemed to be acknowledging another kind of authority. He never saw it before when he needed and wanted to be so right that he stayed inside the ballroom, too concerned with keeping everything as it had always been.

As he is relaxing in the courtyard, he overhears a conversation on quantum physics and health. Listening more closely he overhears someone say, "Our bodies are not really solid mass, but made up of slowed down light waves that respond to our thoughts and feelings—which affect our state of health physically...."

"What?" Now he is sure these people are quite odd. "They think they are light? They truly think they are light! Well," he thinks, "maybe I'd better go back inside, even if it could mean continued illness....and perhaps death."

So, feeling overwhelmed he starts back

toward the ballroom, confused by what he heard, and convinced of the radicalism that is taking place in the courtyard. He tries so hard not to be noticed as he is working his way back inside, that he doesn't notice two of his associates going quickly past him out to the courtyard. One wants to find a way to save the life of his child, and another that of his wife. They are so desperate they are willing to listen to almost anything. In fact, they don't waste time just standing shyly around the perimeters because it isn't just their life; it is the life of those they love, and, with open minds, they walk right into the middle of a group of people in the courtyeard and say, "I'm looking for alternative thinkers."

Everyone raises their hand.

"How could this have been going on?" they say to each other, "I had no idea!"

"What do you want to know?" the people say. As the associates mingle, each begins to meet physicists and doctors and clergymen and housewives and artists and painters and musicians, marketing experts,

business people, actors, writers, public speakers, singers, dancers, healers, lawyers, carpenters and writers. They begin to listen, learn and understand about mind, body, and spirit. They also learn that the mind, the attitude, the thoughts that are facilitated by each individual being, can heal or make ill—any individual.

They are stunned, for many of their beliefs are challenged, and they struggle, comparing their own experience and the new information, with the weight of their collectively formed beliefs of their pasts. Returning to the ballroom, they are hard pressed to discuss these new concepts with their friends and relatives; except that they each find there are books on these concepts they never noticed before, but which had been available to help further understanding. All this is going on, as well as people who you would least suspect, were also looking for new, safe places to share and tell of their discoveries, learnings, and insights; people from all creeds and walks of life were seeking spiritual knowledge, attending

workshops and classes to learn and gain insight.

Gradually the boundaries of the ball of life are expanding, along with the perception and remembrance of those in attendance. As their belief in the more they cannot see grows, the wisdom and knowledge of their divinity is awakening within people.... One by one the memory of spirit and the extraordinary abilities and powers are returning to them, creating many new realities from the divine, spiritual, magic-like human powers that are evolving upon the earth. And, at the ball of life, the human experience elevates to its Godly origin and intent...creating the happiness, joy—and peace within people—that shall bring the much desired peace upon the earth.

As SPIRIT, *before we entered the ball, before we selected our very first costume, and before we selected the one we are wearing now, we were all part of a collective choice to implement reminders along life's way, so*

———

that eventually we would remember that the body is a costume. The ability to think more positive thoughts becomes easier now because people in the ball are learning and remembering the divine power of mind in affirmations and prayers.

As the awareness is gradually awakening, through all individuals, the collective conscious follows. What used to be in fairy tales will return to be known and seen. The fairy / gnome kingdom, the angelic realm, all kindred to people will be known more in awareness, because these realms are of a lighter, higher form of energy vibration, or frequency that people themselves are beginning to facilitate, therefore lifting and changing the density of a third dimension reality, allowing themselves to perceive more that also exists within a fourth dimension and beyond....

Being in a body in the third dimension is wonderful and important, for it allows us to be creative in a physical sense. It allows us to love one another, so that God can have arms to put around another human being for hugs to happen; as well, we could feel a soft breeze against the skin, and we could feel the warmth of the sun upon us; so we could smell the fragrance of glorious flowers in the spring, as well as the whiteness of the silent snow in our winter, kick the brightly colored leaves of fall, and hear the cry of a newborn babe and know another Divine Spirit has come to earth in an act of celebrating creation. ❏

Humans evolved, cultures advanced,
knowledge accumulated...
and all the while, because humans
were also divine,
the whole of the world,
the mind of God,
moved with them.

Voyage of the Soul

To remember all we know,
enjoying life's dance of the spirit

THE VOYAGE OF THE SOUL can also be known as a journey of life as it is told here in the story of the soul that sets forth on a voyage upon the golden waters. In the beginning, the soul and vessel glide out with great anticipation, for a journey of great distance lies before them, and it is full of various possibilities. Oftentimes, however, a strong gale comes from the Eastern winds.

The Gale wind blows the vessel seemingly off its course, and, not noticing the new one there is to see or learn from, or not even questioning the reason the wind blew, the "why" of this experience, this vessel that houses the soul instead tries very hard to get back precisely on its previous course. It is intent on doing only what seems familiar and safe, what it was told it was supposed to do. It continues along the water, being very careful to follow all the rules and keep on course. However, this gale does blow and deviate it again, and instead of looking to see what can be seen from this further change in its course, for he lacks wisdom and is young in that which is his soul's journeys, he tries to go back, out of fear of change, to what was familiar to him; he is very concerned with doing the same as other vessels he shares the waters with— and he goes right back to his course, the one originated before, the one he was very sure he should do.

Something eventually happens over the long course of the journey upon the horizons of the golden waters of life. The spirit starts to become ever so slightly weathered, metaphorically speaking, and seasoned. The rigidity of its course, his attempt to keep on such a narrow course wears down his ability to hold very steady as he once could.

Eventually, over time, through the seasons of this process, the soul becomes less and less fixed upon its original course. Due to the gale winds that so consistently and effortlessly blow upon him, deviating him out of course.

At times like this he begins to notice more and more the golden light and its beauty, which actually creates a glow on the water he sails upon.... He becomes a wiser and more seasoned vessel, and he starts to sense he has been upon such water before; he begins to wonder about the very thing that he does sail through...this water, this sea of consciousness. What creates it, and what, indeed, is it doing here, and why, and who determines the course of his journey?

Now what was once considered by him an important concern: to keep rigidly fixed upon his course, he now seldom even thinks about; this is because of his new preoccupation, his curiosity about what actually creates the golden waters, the very sea of this journey. The soul wonders: when did it start, this journey? for it does not quite

wholly recall; and also, by the way, where was it that he was going? And why..., oh why was there such a hurry? He could not quite recall now why he had to sail such a straight and very rigid path. Where was he going in such a short time?

He had also noticed that there were many other vessels upon the same water, and, from time to time, much to his chagrin, he even noticed a few of them that had sunk, and he would wonder why he had not himself. Why was he still gliding ahead? Who determined which one would sink and which would glide?

He also found that there were seemingly some vessels older and more tattered, more damaged than others. The more the vessel began to speculate on all there was on the journey, and all the interesting occurences, the infinite possibilities, the more the destination became harder and harder to remember: and the less it was remembered, the more he became present, in the now; he felt at ease and peace wherever he was, in any given moment of his journey; and there

became a richness to this soul and to those moments.

Soon this soul began to realize something very fascinating; that at times, when he cast his gaze and focused, looking far ahead on the ocean, it was as if he became instantly there already. Or, when he contemplated where he had been on any part of his journey, he was there as well. And he began to realize he could be at any time or any place in the journey he chose, by simply contemplating it, which became very perplexing to a such a very astute vessel.

Why? Because he had so formulated what he believed he was stuck in the rut of only thinking what he believed; until, of course, he became more curious and questioned the existence of things, and then he found his way to be only one of the many possibilities he had, now there seemed to be more...in fact, so many more choices that what had been reality, as he experienced it...was, he discovered, changeable—and, what is more surprising, he somehow had something to do with that.

—

Well then what is the point of it all? He began again to contemplate. "What is the point of myself and this journey? and the golden waters? Oh, yes, and that gale wind that would arise seemingly from nowhere and blow me off my course… that now I would so welcome—where has it been lately? I could use a new direction, a good adventure." He contemplated all this, until he realized he could choose any direction he desired, even an adventure of a gale wind without the struggle. He could simply choose a change and go off of course. Ah! a revelation.

Well, if he could choose to go out of the norm, to go off of course, could he choose other things? Could he choose already to be at his destination? Hmm. If he could, then it must be so…. If it must be so, then what is it all for…?

"Maybe…maybe I am to simply enjoy this journey! Maybe this journey is meant to be so much, much more. If I just remember that I can have choices… and actually help in creating the reality, the journey…which,

———

perhaps, is more important than the destination.... I think this is the something...long ago I vaguely couldn't quite remember...."

— ❧ —

FROM TIME TO TIME, to go off of course and explore life and its many possibilities, affords a person something he or she may not be aware of presently. People could expand their perception of life and see their choices increase.... ❏

Like the genie
who sits within Alladin's lamp,
awaiting to grant each command...
so as well a power sits within all,
granting every wish, thought and
prayer... for this power ...
you must know...
is divinely shared

*Thoughts to Charm the Mind and
Heart and Speak to the Soul*

— 🍃 —

*and the genie speaks on
Sacred Knowledge and Daily Living*

It is for you to know, to enter into a place
of prayer and to ask for and draw to you
what you desire; and surrender unto that
which is God, your love and your willingness
to realize the full potential of your soul,
accepting divine guidance for your destiny,
for the highest and the greatest good of you
and mankind. Let this be your truth to be
lived in this your hour.

The Heavens and the Earth

Walk more on the earth with bare feet, and feel the earth's energy and let it communicate to you. The sun and moon, the stars and clouds, all reflect their cosmic energy upon it and the earth gives this all back to us through our food, our sustenance.

It is well to do this often, this walk of communication and be among the elements of nature. Sleep where there is nothing between you and the heavens and stars but your love of God.... Let the moonlight and stars beacon to your spirit's remembrance of its soul's place with God.... Let the vibrations be felt and laid upon the vibration of the lights that dwell within the cells of your body. Let the cells and the light of yourself and the lights of the heavens and stars dance together, for it accelerates one's remembrance.

There is something like an unseen blueprint within the vibration of the soul. When one sleeps under the roofed dwelling too often, one closes oneself off from that which feeds the spirit.... People do not live by bread alone, but also by beauty and love. Many are malnourished and need what is free and is here for us in abundance to sustain the human spirit.

Feel the earth, touch it, stand on it, lay on it, and look to the heavens. Let the stars be your blanket, the moon your comforter, and still yourself often to absorb the silent beauty of the sunsets and sunrises. All of these are here to resonate remembrance that cannot be found in a written word, in a spoken word, in books or in halls of learning. I am speaking of the balance that must come back into our lives to support us to live as spiritual beings.

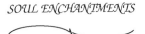

Contemplate these wisdoms many, many times. For each time that you do, you will hear more, realize more, experience more. It is living truth; it accommodates every phase and every level you go to. And it will hold the test of all time, because it holds potency for great inspiration.Once you are inspired, you will hear the more and feel the more, and onward to yours and God's glory you will find yourself.

The Mystery of You

Stay steadfast on your course to understand yourself. You are the most important mystery you will ever solve.

— 🜓 —

Healing

All have the power to heal, because all have the power to get sick. Illness is less natural and it takes more effort.

— 🜓 —

Self Mystery

Stay steadfast on your course to understand yourself. You are the most important mystery that you can solve.

Personal Destiny

Among the benefits of enlightenment is the joy found in the awareness of Divine choice. To live this understanding fully is to then make conscious choices in support of your fulfillment in life, consciously directing the course of your own destiny in support of itself.

Consciousness

Each individual person, through consciousness, adds to the whole of the collective consciousness, of which all are in effect.

Choices

Are you living the life of your choice, or someone else's choices for you?

Imagination

Give honor to your imagination. God talks to you there. Imagination is not only a place in which you can dream and create, but also one where you receive vision and guidance.

That which dwells with God, though not in form, that is of light and twinkles, that truly does exist, loves, and dwells there in the imagination as well. People need not be fearful they will lose their mind, but rather that they will expand it to rediscover and include the more they have for so long been shut down to....

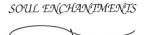

Awakening

Do more quality living in your daily life, and make the choices that create more of the moments when you feel elevated and inspired beyond space and time. These moments will then fuel the transformation and the awakening of your soul to the "more." Speak often with God, and yourself, about what you want.

— ❧ —

Importance of Being You

There is a story you have not heard, a book you have not read, a movie you have not seen, and it is based... on your own life. Take the time to research your own existence, as if you and your life were as significant as any famous person of history ... because it is.

Inspiration

Have the courage to believe that you can do whatever your soul, your spirit has been inspiring and rallying you to do. The inspiration is always accompanied by the ability to fulfill itself.

— ❦ —

Walls Built by Attitudes

For greater understanding, explore your mind, and push outwardly all the perimeters that limit it. Look over the wall that has been built around it, through many thousands of years and various cultural beliefs, peek over the side; you'll then perhaps find not only that there is more. You may find what you have been wanting, were it not for the walls. Climb over them.

Ability

Ability does not dwell with just one alone. It is marvelous to be a spirit human and know that one is not confined to what it is humans think they cannot do. Through your spirit you can access all that has ever been done and all ever created—which dwells within the collective consciousness, always to be fed upon and fed back to. All that has been invented, came first through thought. All prophecy, all poetry, all literature, all art, all music..., dwells within consciousness. Thus, with desire, the ability, the talent, the gifts and the host of that which has done this before is there for one to draw upon to fuel one's own individual creativity.

Self Trust

Take joy in hearing words that you have long found resonated to your soul. Know you have been right in your heart and in your quiet moments more than you have been wrong. It is not disloyalty to rethink inherited truths from the past. Put your mind to the task of where you will harvest.

Careers

In the years that are coming new careers are needed, because the previously destructive activities will fall by the wayside.

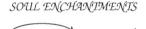

— 💛 —

Leap of Faith

You must spiritually prepare yourselves in your own minds, by inner prayer, by positive thoughts and desires, to be positioned for your highest and greatest good, which includes the highest good for all life on the whole of earth. You should follow your inspiration and take the leap of strong faith and implement your individual plans.

— 💛 —

Miracles

Miracles are found where faith is at its highest. There is something wonderful about faith and romance that is good to understand. It is that they engage us in an altered state that renders us more receptive to the higher frequencies of thought that exist within the mind of God we all share.

———

Guidance

The more one feels attuned to life, and the more one feels touched by their own spirit, the more one will be able to feel and be touched by the guidance of higher spirit, which is indeed to one's benefit.

Oneness

Because individual consciousness and the collective consciousness move to oneness, the unification that takes place in the psyche expresses out into actions, beliefs, and words. The result of this is heightened awareness, heightened attunement, a sensitivity to the world.

Celebrate the Differences

Instead of judging each other's costume, it would be good to admire the differences, so that everyone begins to want to be as unique as they are. Can you imagine such a place?

Acceptability

Would it mean that we would no longer have our youth needing to take drugs, and extreme substances in order to endure the harshness of the life that has been here? Can it be that whoever they are and however they express is acceptable?

Can you imagine feeling you are accepted and loved just as you are—and in whatever way you are expressing? It truly makes no way wrong before this time. It makes every way contribute to this hour.

Receiving

It has been said that the universe is abundant and affluent. It is the various beliefs and frameworks of human beings that can create blocks of how this can get to them. There are many and varied wants and desires, but the individual attitudes and belief system in it can even restrict the whole of the universe, which must find its way through them in order to accomodate one's prayer, or request. If one finds oneself praying and asking for something, and seemingly finds this has not been answered, one should ask oneself: is there an adequate opening? Or, is there simply a little pinhole through which I can receive? If the universe always says "yes...." are you agreeing as well as asking?

Personal Communion

Reading or listening to various prayers and affirmations created by others can be inspiring; however, what comes from the deep well of one's own being, with true emotion, finds expression through the thoughts and words of an individual. This is the supreme prayer because it is filled with each individual's pure sentiments, filled with personal emotions and love. The vibration of such action, by its very nature, will align oneself to the divine vibration centered within the Isness of God. Many prayers are to inspire and assist others into sacred communion. Once led there, it is for each individual to continue their sacred journey, of their own expression, and develop their own personal relationship with God.

The Mind

Where does the mind of the individual end and the mind of God begin. . . ? At the perimeters of each individual's awareness. Thus it is for each a choice to know or not the mind and perceptions of God. Ask that the mind of God shall become more personally known, increasingly penetrating one's mind, developing trust over doubt and faith over fear. Commit not just to your belief in God, but also to your belief that God is committed to you.

Grace of Change

Through the grace and the glory of God, which is being realized by hundreds more people now than ever before, people of the world are afforded the grace of a vibration that will wave over them like a soft breeze. This breeze will infiltrate their beingness, dance with the atoms and molecules of their bodies, lift their lights, cradle their hearts, inspire their souls, and illuminate their minds with an ever greater force than those who came before them... and who helped put this wave into motion.

Prayer

Prayer is thought. It influences the world and the immediate environment. Just do it.

— ❦ —

Spirit

We have a body, we have a mind, we have an intellect, and we have a heart so we can feel our way about things and we can reason things. But the central command of reasoning, thinking and feeling is our spirit. And our spirit comes from a realm that is invisible, into a body that is visible, to participate in creation.

— ❦ —

Thirst for the Divine

Commenting on the value of being, a wise teacher once said, "I laugh when I see the fish in the water are thirsty."

— ❦ —

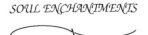

Righteousness

"True righteousness" does not mean the attitude that places oneself above others, but rather the righteousness of one who lives in harmony with God and uses this awareness and its power to help their fellow beings.

— ❦ —

Command of Spirit

We have a body, we have a mind, we have an intellect, and we have a heart so we can sense and feel our way about things. But the central command of reasoning, thinking and feeling is our spirit. Our spirit comes from a realm that is invisible... that enters into a body that is visible, to live and create in the realities of a third dimensional world.

— ❦ —

Consciousness

Consciousness consists of energy. Energy is indefatigable. It is attitude that gets fatigued.

— ❦ —

Earth Sustenance

Sacred and natural knowledge of the earth is held within us from the food, the sustenance we've always since birth consumed. The sacred beating sounds of drums help release this knowledge within our being. During or after ceremonies of song or drumming as in the Native American culture, people find themselves more comforted and knowing from this natural reconnecting with the mother earth and its knowledge. Thus there is a balance found in music combining the celestial voice in song and earth connection through drumming.

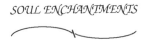

Love of God

From time to time, remember to sleep under an open sky, with nothing between you and the stars but your love of God.

Speed Bumps

People are often perplexed by the "lag time" that often seems to exist between their desire and its actual manifestation; this lag time is often the result of their own attitudes, which act like speed bumps in the road their life.

Self Intimacy

Value and cherish and most intimately acquaint yourself with our own soul, for it is your vehicle unto forever. . . .

— 🐛 —

Illusion and Reality

It is important that the illusion of life in all of its beauty and grandness must not override the knowledge of the reality of your spirit.

— 🐛 —

Miracles

Miracles are found where faith is at its highest.

— 🐛 —

Self Healing

When people feel their most absolute joyous, they should focus and sustain this feeling as long as possible, and feel it throughout the body for in the state of joy, the body releases what is needed to heal itself.

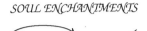

— ❦ —

Feeling

The more one feels touched by their own spirit, the more one will be able to feel and be touched by the guidance of higher spirit, which is indeed to one's benefit.

— ❦ —

Uniqueness

Can you imagine feeling loved and accepted just as you are?...if you can...you have started in the most important place.

Participation

Remember, we participate in the answers to our own and others' prayers. Often people don't feel worthy for what they ask; then they make it difficult for themselves to receive. The universe, the creator, which created what is love, happiness, joy, says "yes." It is human will, individual choice that also determines how the universe says "yes" and awaits.

Restraint and Direction

If you are still struggling with the emotions that you feel are negative or unkind, keep them silent, and choose a different thought, refraining from giving it the power of voice.

Doubt

Throughout history people have taken many treasures to lay at the feet of their Gods. These, they believed, would hold great value, and they hoped the Gods would recognize the sincerity. Rarely did the people bring their doubt—yet so many hang on to it as their greatest treasure. Give over your doubt to God and go and truly live your faith. Believe in happiness.

Spiritual Teaching

Being a good spiritual leader or teacher requires not only love of God and understanding divine knowledge, but also understanding the delicate web of human frailties and applying such wisdom with the same caring and reverence as one would of God. . . for surely what is considered sacred must include people. . .

Awakening and Sleeping

Begin each day upon your wakening and acknowledge the glory of God that has expressed itself as you, that you might know it greater and express it purer.

Each night before you enter into your slumber, think of your day and how you would make your tomorrow even greater. Ask that that which is the light of God be known to you as your light, and God's love, your love, and God's healing, your ability to heal, so that your last and your first thoughts of your day of awakened state are anointed appropriately, and to assure that before you enter into your slumber, that all things will advance your awakening into the greater glory of who you are, that your existence might enhance the human experience for the glory of God and humanity.

From those in the Highest of High...
and the ancient one's twinkling of an eye...
joined with the swirling smoke from
Alladin's lamp...echoes a
message of fare thee well and goodbye...
until yet another time...:

Now that we have brought unto you a
multitude of wisdoms it is for you to
contemplate them many, many times, for
each time that you do, you shall hear more,
realize more, and experience more. This that
we have shared unto you is living truth that
shall accommodate every phase and every
level of your existence. These wisdoms will
stand the test of time, and they hold within
them the potency for great inspiration, and
once you are thus divinely inspired, you
shall hear the more and feel the more of all
that is to remember, and onward to yours
and God's glory, you will find yourself....

Personal Remembrances

Personal Notes:_____

_____

_____

_____

_____

_____

_____

_____

_____

_____

_____

_____

_____

_____

_____

_____

_____

*Personal Notes:*_____

_____

_____

_____

_____

_____

_____

_____

_____

_____

_____

_____

_____

_____

_____

_____

_____

_____

_____

_____

_____

SOUL ENCHANTMENTS

Personal Notes:_____

_____

_____

_____

_____

_____

_____

_____

_____

_____

_____

_____

_____

_____

_____

_____

_____

_____

_____

_____

_____

*Personal Notes:*_____

_____

_____

_____

_____

_____

_____

_____

_____

_____

_____

_____

_____

_____

_____

_____

_____

_____

SOUL ENCHANTMENTS

Personal Notes: _____

_____

_____

_____

_____

_____

_____

_____

_____

_____

_____

_____

_____

_____

_____

_____

_____

___

*Personal Notes:*_____

_____

_____

_____

_____

_____

_____ ___

_____

_____

_____

_____

_____

_____

_____

_____

_____

_____

_____

_____

SOUL ENCHANTMENTS

*Personal Notes:*_____

_____

_____

_____

_____

_____

_____

_____

_____

_____

_____

_____

_____

_____

_____

_____

_____

_____

_____

_____

_____

_____

_____

*Personal Notes:*_____

_____

_____

_____

_____

_____

_____

_____

_____

_____

_____

_____

_____

_____

_____

_____

_____

_____

_____

_____

_____

Childhood Promises to Keep

Personal Notes: _____

_____

_____

_____

_____

_____

_____

_____

_____

_____

_____

_____

_____

_____

_____

_____

_____

_____

Personal Notes: _____

_____

_____

_____

_____

_____

_____

_____

_____

_____

_____

_____

_____

_____

_____

_____

_____

_____

_____

_____

SOUL ENCHANTMENTS

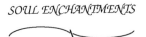

*Personal Notes:*_____

_____

_____

_____

_____

_____

_____

_____

_____

_____

_____

_____

_____

_____

_____

_____

_____

_____

———

*Personal Notes:*_____

_____

_____

_____

_____

_____

_____

_____

_____

_____

_____

_____

_____

_____

_____

_____

_____

_____

_____

___

SOUL ENCHANTMENTS

*Personal Notes:*_____

_____

_____

_____

_____

_____

_____

_____

_____

_____

_____

_____

_____

_____

_____

_____

_____

_____

_____

_____

_____

_____

*Personal Notes:*_____

_____

_____

_____

_____

_____

_____

_____

_____

_____

_____

_____

_____

_____

_____

_____

_____

_____

_____

SOUL ENCHANTMENTS

*Personal Notes:*_____

_____

_____

_____

_____

_____

_____

_____

_____

_____

_____

_____

_____

_____

_____

_____

_____

_____

_____

_____

———

*Personal Notes:*_____

_____

_____

_____

_____

_____

_____

_____

_____

_____

_____

_____

_____

_____

_____

_____

_____

_____

_____

———

Beyond Common Thought-the joy of being you

In ten eloquent chapters, this book covers the topics of humankind's long search for meaning, peace on earth, free will, choice of destiny, the frontiers of consciousness and man's role as a co-creator. It speaks to the wave of questioning among a world of people at this time like no other time before.

"...unfolding an awareness rarely available...Jacqueline...(has) a divine gift that enables her to bring forth the mysteries of the universe with an amazing ease."
> — **Ambassador G.M. Nhigula,** Member of Parliament, Tanzania

"...will bring love and inspiration to all who read it."
> — **Louise Hay**, author of *You Can Heal Your Life*

"...so much wisdom in your words and thoughts. Please keep writing."
> — **Brian L. Weiss**, M.D., P.A. author of *Many Lives, Many Masters*

"The time seems especially ripe for the people of the earth everywhere to hear and feel this great message so that they can live in harmony with the true cosmic law and help each other. ... written with enthusiasm and feeling and deserves to be widely read!"
> —**Ravi Ravindra,** Ph.D., Prof. of Religion and Physics., Dalhousie Univ.

"...excellent reading material on...the unknown within ourselves."
> — **Erica Mann**, Exec. Vice Chairman, Council for Human Ecology, Kenya

❧

AUTHOR AVAILABILITY: Jacqueline T. Snyder is available for workshops, private or group counseling, lectures and seminars.

❧

Share these wonderful books with your friends:

Beyond Common Thought (Softcover, 202 pgs)
      Qty _____ @ $13.95 each $_____

Soul Enchantments (Softcover, 112 pgs)
      Qty _____ @ $7.95 each $_____
      Shipping $3.50 for one book $_____
      + $.50 each add'l copy to same address $_____
      Washington residents: .082 sales tax $_____

Total Enclosed (payable to CADCM) $_____

Please put my name on your Mailing List:

Name_____

Address_____

City_____State_____Zip_____

Windsor House Publishers/ CADCM
P.O. Box 409, Maple Valley, WA 98038 • (206) 432-5412

 **Jacqueline Snyder,** author of *Beyond Common Thought, the joy of being you* is truly a pioneer in consciousness. She has eloquently taken ancient wisdoms and beliefs pondered for centuries by humanity, expanding and simplifying them into new paradigms of thought that encompass all realms of life. *Beyond Common Thought* is singularly brilliant in its depth and breadth of understanding of human nature, and the rethinking of God and self into a greater meaning. It has received acclaim in the scientific, medical, philosophical and spiritual communities for its clarity, wisdom and insight.

Her second book, *Soul Enchantments, Mystical Stories to Charm Remembrance,* is a delightful reading experience, weaving profound spiritual knowledge through a series of magical stories and thought-provoking quotes, brilliantly charming the mind and heart with thoughts that speak to the soul.

A woman of great vision and inspiration, Jacqueline Snyder lectures internationally in the field of spirituality. Her brilliant mind and strong intuitive abilities render her a dynamic communicator and teacher of spiritual knowledge. With a natural love and enthusiasm for life, she conveys her reverence for God, life and the individual spirit.

Jacqueline also enjoys a nationwide private practice in spiritual counseling. A skilled clinical hypnotherapist as well, she finds hypnotherapy to be a valuable tool in personal counseling and group sessions for resolving issues held in the subconscious mind, as well as assisting an individual to access higher states of divine consciousness in support of their ultimate potential. She is also the founder and president of the Association for Spiritual and Clinical Hypnotherapists.

Ms. Snyder resides in Washington State with her two sons.